Walkthrough

Let's look at th[...]
today is abou[...]
(point to the name) a[...]
all point to the turtle on the cover of [...]
book?

Phonic Opportunity

Ling is a lovely name, isn't it? Can you think of some words that rhyme with 'Ling'?

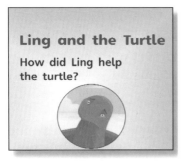

Walkthrough

Let's look at the back cover. Can you point to the blurb on the back cover?

Read the blurb.

How do you think Ling might help the turtle in this story?

Walkthrough

Let's turn to the title page. Can you read the title of the book with me?

Read the title.

Oh dear, how do you think the turtle is feeling in this illustration? Why?

Walkthrough

Where is the turtle? Do you think she needs some help?
Who might help her?

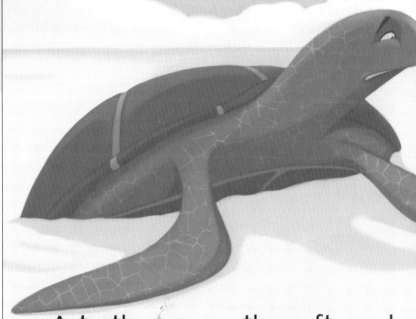

A turtle was on the soft sand.

2

 Observe and Prompt

Word Recognition

(P) Encourage the children to use their decoding skills to sound out and blend the phonemes in 'soft' and 'sand' to read the words.

- If children struggle with 'turtle', tell them this word and model how to decode it.

- Check that children can recognise and independently read the sight words 'was' and 'the'.

3

👁 Observe and Prompt

Language Comprehension

- Check that children understand what the problem might be for the turtle stuck in the soft sand.

Walkthrough

The poor turtle is shouting for help here. She is sinking into the sand.
What might she be saying?

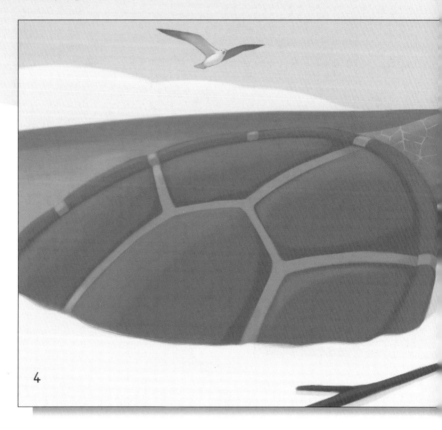

4

 Observe and Prompt

Word Recognition

> Ⓟ Check that the children are using their decoding skills to
> help them sound out and blend all through the word
> 'Help'. Some children may be able to read 'sinking' in the
> same way; if they struggle, help children with this word.
>
> ● Check that children can recognise and independently read
> the sight words 'she' and 'said'.

Can you see someone in the illustration who might be able to help?

"Help me!" she said.
"I am sinking."

5

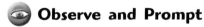 **Observe and Prompt**

Language Comprehension

● Check that the children use appropriate expression when reading the turtle's words.

Walkthrough

What did Ling do? He lifted the turtle out. Can you see what he used to help the turtle?

Ling lifted her out.

6

 Observe and Prompt

Word Recognition

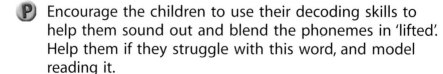 Encourage the children to use their decoding skills to help them sound out and blend the phonemes in 'lifted'. Help them if they struggle with this word, and model reading it.

6

Walkthrough

What do you think the turtle said to Ling after he lifted her out?

"Thank you," said the turtle.

7

 **Observe and Prompt**

Language Comprehension

- Check that children can describe what is happening in the story.
- How do they think Ling and the turtle are feeling?

Walkthrough

Who can describe what's happening in this picture?
Introduce the word 'junk' and point to it in the picture.
Why is Ling looking scared?

The next day,
Ling was out in his junk.

8   9

 Observe and Prompt

Word Recognition

P Encourage the children
to use their decoding
skills to help them read
'next', 'day', 'Ling' and
'junk'.

● The words 'the', 'was' and
'out' are sight words –
check that the children
recognise and can read
these independently.

Language Comprehension

● Check that the children
can tell you what is
happening in the story at
this point, and explain
why Ling might be scared.

8

Walkthrough

What is happening to Ling? Turn back to page 5 and reread what the turtle said. Match the words to those on page 11. Ling is saying the same thing, here, isn't he?

"Help me!" he said.
"I am sinking!"

10

11

Observe and Prompt

Word Recognition

P Encourage the children to use their decoding skills to read the words 'help' and 'sinking'.

Language Comprehension

● Check that children can explain the danger that Ling is in and predict what might happen next.

9

Walkthrough

What has the turtle done for Ling? How do you think Ling felt when he was lifted on top of the turtle's shell?

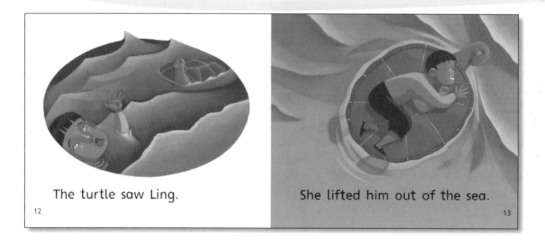

The turtle saw Ling.

12

She lifted him out of the sea.

13

Observe and Prompt

Word Recognition

P Check that the children use their decoding skills to sound out and blend all through the words 'Ling' and 'lifted'.

● 'The', 'saw', 'she', 'out' and 'of' are sight words – check that the children recognise and read these independently.

Language Comprehension

● Encourage the children to explain how the characters are feeling at this point in the story.

● Why do the children think the turtle came back to help Ling?

Walkthrough

The turtle is taking Ling back to his junk. What do you think Ling might say to the turtle?

She took Ling back to the junk.

14   15

Observe and Prompt

Word Recognition

- Check that children can use their decoding skills to read 'Ling', 'back' and 'junk'.

Language Comprehension

- Ask the children what they think might happen next.

Walkthrough

What do you think Ling and the turtle are saying?

"Thank you," said Ling.
"Thank you," said the turtle.

16

 Observe and Prompt

Word Recognition

- Encourage children to sound out and blend all through the word 'thank'.